BERNARD BRIGGS

BASEBALL STAR

"Hey, Ted, I didn't know they cared!"

BRIGGS THE GREATEST

BERNARD BRIGGS, the famous all-round sportsman and star goalkeeper, was on a tour of America. He stopped off at the town of Tontara where he was to help an old friend, Ted Brand, by playing in an important match for the Tontara Terrors, the football team which Ted had just taken over.

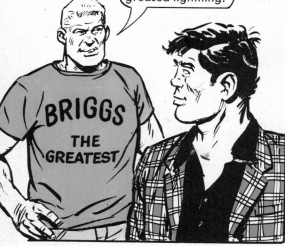

"That's not for you, punk! It's for 'Blue Lightning Briggs' — the greatest baseball pitcher this State's ever seen! He's greased lightning!"

BRIGGS THE GREATEST

SUPPORT THE TONTARA TERRORS

"Here come our lot now, Bernard!"

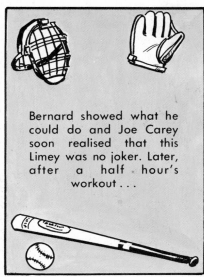

See you Saturday then, Joe!

Bernard showed what he could do and Joe Carey soon realised that this Limey was no joker. Later, after a half hour's workout . . .

You bet, Bernard! And I reckon these Kansas Cowboys ain't gonna ride roughshod over us the way they did last time out!

Later—

Hey, you're the new Limey goalie who's come to help out with the Terrors, ain't ya? Bit of a dealer I hear tell too. Well, I just got the deal for you, bud!

I'm always interested in a deal, sir. Lead me to it!

That's Gold Brick Brogan and Smooth Talkin' Carter in action—best con men in the State. They'll be taking that dumb Limey for a sucker!

There's a fine bit of property—a gentleman like you looking for a deal couldn't do no better than that!

This is a historic building dating from the foundation of Tontara. Full of antiques. Just what a gent like you would be looking for.

The old livery stables! This could be interesting.

Look at all these antiques! Could be worth a fortune! And this is a prime site just the sort of thing for you!

Load of rubbish! But, if my hunch is right . . .

You've done it again Smooth Talkin'! You got that Limey on the hook!

Should be about here, I reckon . . . oh!

Later—,

Well, you sure believe in inspecting property, mister! What do you say? Only twelve hundred dollars for the lot!

I'll give you a thousand!

Done! Shake on it!

This is rich! I'm gonna 'phone the Tribune and tell them how we made a monkey out of that Limey goal-tender!

Next day—

I said we wanted publicity—but not that kind! And that thousand bucks must have been all you had!

TONTARA BUGLE
LIMEY GOALIE TAKEN FOR A SUCKER.
SMOOTH TALKING CARTER DOES IT AGAIN

Don't worry, Ted, mate. I'll make a profit! But I'll need some help from the rest of the lads!

The others were happy to help, and soon . . .

GREAT ANTIQUE SALE
COME ALONG AFTER THE BASEBALL MATCH FOR BARGAINS OF A LIFETIME

JAKE'S BARN

Haw, haw! That's rich! That store's been well gone over and everything worth a cent has been sold!

8

Rounders! This is a real man's game, Limey! You should'a worn your cap 'cause I'm gonna give you a centre parting with my bean ball!

I hope this Limey knows what he's doing. I've never seen Blue Lightning so mad!

Boy, does he know what he's doing! He's belted it right out of the park. No guy's done that to Blue Lightning before!

Bernard completely dominated the game. His catching was superb and his batting finally demoralised Blue Lightning Briggs.

Blue Lightning suffered the ultimate humiliation, he was "yanked", that is, replaced by another pitcher. But the newcomer got the same treatment and the Tigers crushed the Cowboys.

I did you blokes a good turn. Now you help me out! Come to the soccer match tomorrow—and there is a story for you news hawks if you come to the antique sale tonight!

NOW TURN TO PAGE 65.

9

SMUGGLERS' SMILES AND WILES

CIGAR CAR—Early this century a smuggler sneaked a load of cigars from France into England by hiding them in the bodywork of his car. He was found out when the shaft of a horse-drawn omnibus pierced the side of the car at a London Station!

'BACCY TO BOOT—Customs officials were almost beaten by a Chinese seaman suspected of smuggling tobacco into Britain. Then they discovered that he had used it to re-sole a pair of old canvas shoes!

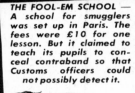

THE FOOL-EM SCHOOL — A school for smugglers was set up in Paris. The fees were £10 for one lesson. But it claimed to teach its pupils to conceal contraband so that Customs officers could not possibly detect it.

ICE-IN SUGAR—A smart American smuggler fooled the Customs by giving a kid a stick of barley-sugar. Once the youngster was through the customs, the smuggler took back the barley-sugar, in which was hidden a fortune in gems.

FORTUNE AFOOT—A New York customs man, suspicious of a bloke who had enormous feet, took him to Customs House. The man's feet turned out to be perfectly normal, but his huge boots contained hiding places for smuggled diamonds!

HOT POTATOES—One warm day Customs men boarded a ship loaded with barrels of potatoes. They found nothing suspicious until a barrel burst and poured out its contents on the deck. In the hot sun the potatoes melted. They were made of wax and concealed pearls and diamonds!

GOLDEN MUDGUARDS—Smugglers used to get gold into Pakistan from the Persian Gulf area by fashioning it into mudguards, which they bolted on to old cars. They painted the mudguards then drove across the border.

THE FLOATING MAN

Amazing! He's sitting on the water, like in an easy chair!

It's only a novelty! There's no commercial value in that suit!

IN the 19th century, Paul Boyton, the Floating Man, travelled the world demonstrating the Merriman Buoyancy Suit. In this, a person could float indefinitely and move anywhere at will. Few people bought the suits but Paul gave demonstrations and took collections. One day in Durban . . .

But two men saw a use for the suit.

Lopez, think what we could do with such equipment.

I agree, Carlo, but we cannot buy such a suit. The price—

You do not think well, Lopez. We need not buy the suit—only borrow it.

THE SEAMAN'S REST

Later, in town.

We are police officers, sir. Has anyone offered to buy one of your suits?

No, I'm sorry to say. Why?

Diamond smuggling is why, Mister Boyton.

Diamonds stolen from the Kimberley mines get smuggled out of the country. We stop lots of smugglers, but think what one of your suits would mean to a thief.

I see. If I sell any suits I'll let you know who buys them.

THE Bella Finka was a Portuguese ship which made regular calls at the larger South African ports. She always anchored outside the three-mile territorial waters limit, and carried men who dealt in precious stones. The South African police knew all about the ship and her trade in stolen diamonds but could do nothing to stop her, as she remained outside their jurisdiction. They tried very hard to make sure that no stolen diamonds were taken out to the ship, but somehow, someone always sneaked past them.

That afternoon.

I'll let the suit dry overnight and pack it away tomorrow. No one here seems keen to buy.

So—contact everyone with diamonds to sell, Lopez. We will guarantee to deliver them to Bella Finka tonight, for ten per cent of the price we get.

Certainly, compadre, but it is the big risk.

Later that day.

Haven't turned up any diamonds yet, today.

No, and that makes me suspicious. We'll double our harbour guards tonight.

12

That night while Boyton slept.

Ha, he sleeps deeply. Good.

Carlo, we have the suit, but there are patrol boats—

Agreed, Lopez, but they look for other boats and they will look in vain.

Your idea is different, but we're not so sure about it, Carlo. So take this small lot of diamonds tonight. If everything works, we'll give you the rest tomorrow night.

As you wish, but it will be easy. I tell you.

After a little practice Carlo headed for the Bella Finka.

Ha! Am I not the clever one!

We've scared off the smugglers. No one's tried to reach the Bella Finka all night.

On board the Bella Finka.

Here's the money for these diamonds. Can we expect you tomorrow night?

Certainly, senor. I will be, without fail.

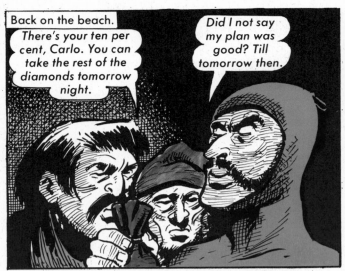

Back on the beach.

There's your ten per cent, Carlo. You can take the rest of the diamonds tomorrow night.

Did I not say my plan was good? Till tomorrow then.

You are magnificent, Carlo.

But of course. Now we return the suit to Senor Boyton—and borrow it again tomorrow night.

I thank you, senor. May you sleep well, every night.

But next morning.

The suit is still wet, and there's water on the floor too. I'll have to have a word with the police about this.

I agree, Mister Boyton. Smugglers could have used your suit to take diamonds out to the Bella Finka. Would you please stay on here and we'll watch in case they try their trick again tonight.

Certainly, officer, but leave it all to me. If it is smugglers I'll give them the fright of their lives.

Boyton set his trap, and that night.

So—my midnight visitor is back again!

Enjoy your ride, mate. You're in for a surprise!

This bag holds every stolen diamond in Durban, Carlo. You'll make at least a thousand pounds tonight, if you pull it off.

What can go wrong, senor? I will return in no time.

With all my money I will buy a Merriman Suit, and become the best and richest smuggler in all Africa!

I will—what happens? I grow big!

Help! Help! Lopez! Compadres! Police! Anybody! Help! Help!

What's this? Hey, is he a smuggler?

Get hold of him, Constable. Use a boat hook!

I got him! Look, he's sprung a leak!

Phew! What a smell! Don't strike a light or we'll all go up with a bang. That's acetylene gas!

Ah, lots of lovely diamonds! Caught you at last, Carlo. You shouldn't have borrowed Mister Boyton's floating suit.

I admit to all things, only get me out of this evil-smelling contraption.

A good night's work for us, Mister Boyton, but we've punctured your suit.

A rubber patch will fix that, Sergeant. A good thing about the Merriman suit is that it's so easy to repair.

We pay a reward for recovering stolen diamonds. Ten per cent of the value of the stones, so you get about a thousand pounds.

Well, that's great, Sergeant. Many thanks!

Now, tell me, how did you fix that suit to swell up like that?

Simple, really. I opened one of the buoyancy chambers and filled it with calcium carbide. When the water got to it, the carbide gave off acetylene gas. And the whole suit ballooned up!

There he goes, Sarge. That Merriman suit is a great idea.

I can think of one man who wouldn't agree with you. He's in jail!

16

The End

19

20

21

22

23

SERGEANT HANNAH V.C.

September 15, 1940—Hampden bombers of the R.A.F. launched a night attack on German barge concentrations in Antwerp, Belgium.

Turning for final approach . . .

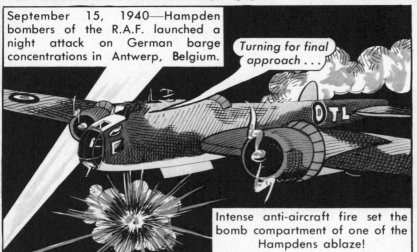

Intense anti-aircraft fire set the bomb compartment of one of the Hampdens ablaze!

The rear-gunner baled out, but Sergeant Hannah, the wireless operator stayed to fight the flames.

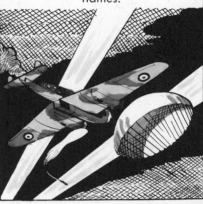

With thousands of rounds of ammunition exploding around him, Hannah disregarded severe burns and eventually quelled the fire, beating at it with the navigator's log when the extinguishers were finished.

The navigator has baled out, skipper. Here's the charts! Now get us home, I'm whacked.

The bomber came safely home. For his courage Sergeant Hannah—aged only 18—was awarded the highest honour, the Victoria Cross.

NO WAR FOR WILBUR

"Look out, Wilbur, you'll have us in the drink."

"If these pesky seagulls would get out of the way I'd get a better shot at that U-boat's periscope."

WILBUR WATSON, barnstorming American pilot, was turned down by the R.A.F. at the start of World War II because of his lack of book learning. He became a civilian pilot with the Air Transport Auxiliary and had a knack of getting in on the action, everywhere. One day, Wilbur and his navigator, ex-R.A.F. man Horace Hinks, approached their base in England with a Hudson they had brought from Canada.

Wilbur always wore cowboy gear and a brace of six-guns.

"That periscope is an impossible target, Wilbur, even for you. Let's head on for England."

"Not likely, Horace. If I can put out that U-boat's eye it'll have to surface. And that'll give our guys in that convoy a better chance."

Wilbur went in again.

"Yippee! I knew I could do it. Now you can't see, Jerry."

We winged it, Horace, and now—yikes!

Talk about the U-boat being winged! So are we! Look at this mess—

Yeah! It's called a bird-strike. Ugh!—these feathers. Hey, we've lost power on an engine.

Hours later.

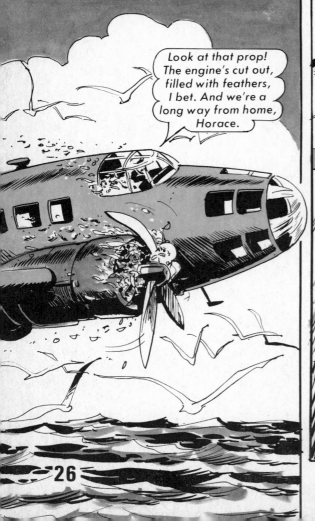

Look at that prop! The engine's cut out, filled with feathers, I bet. And we're a long way from home, Horace.

Phew! We've made it at last. Can you get us down, Wilbur?

Sit tight, Horace! I never left anybody up here yet.

A new Lysander to be delivered, Watson. The airfield is hush-hush and difficult to find, so I'll navigate for you.

Right, boss, anything you say.

A nice, steady take-off. Wilbur's going to be on his best behaviour with the boss aboard.

Another Lysander ahead, boss.

That'll be from the airfield, come to guide us in.

Follow—urr! What are you playing at?

Jerry intruder! Me110 gunning for us, boss!

CRACK

29

Guess we've found the airfield. But they sure ain't flying heavy bombers outa this cabbage patch.

It's run by Special Operations Executive. They ferry secret agents in and out of Occupied France.

We have an agent waiting to be picked up in France tonight. The Jerries are after him. But now we've lost pilot and plane.

You've got this Lizzie, captain. I'll go!

You can't do it, Watson. You're a civilian.

So's the guy whose life may depend on being picked up tonight. There ain't no choice, boss, I gotta go!

That night, Wilbur was over France.

That's the signal from the Resistance guys.

Not exactly a super flarepath, but it'll do!

Glad to see you, chum. Crikey, a flying cowboy!

Howdy, pal! Introductions later!

Suddenly.

The Huns have found us! We will hold them off! Go, mon ami!

Roger! Good luck, pal!

We're hit!

Yeah, but still flying!

Searchlights and flak! We've sure stirred things up!

The End

WILSON

Follow me, Tom! You can do it!

Another amazing adventure of the World's wonder athlete!

Well done! We'll soon have you as good as new!

I feel second-hand right now! I'm a miler not a bloomin' long jumper!

A good athlete is good at most events and you're a good athlete, Tom!

I was—and I just hope I can get my form back!

Tom Vale was one of Britain's top milers. Injured in a car crash, he had come to Saughton Castle Convalescent Home in a bid to get back to full fitness. Wilson, the famous wonder athlete, helped out at the castle which was run by his friend, Dr. Martin Roberts.

It's starting to rain. That'll put paid to my swim!

Never mind, Tom. Come with me. I've something to show you!

This is really something, Tom.

BEAGLE AND ADVER

Mr. Ted Jay recalls memories and stories of his past. He says he saw a soldier, Corporal Parr, run a mile, walk a mile, and swim a mile—all in under half an hour.

There it is, Tom. In that item about Mister Jay—

The old boy must be imagining things! Nobody could have done these things in that time! I don't believe it!

I do, Tom!

Let's have a run over to Lamprie and have a word with the old chap.

But it's ten miles across the moors— and it's pouring rain!

On the outskirts of Lamprie they slipped into a barn and changed their clothes before calling on Mr. Ray.

It was no use arguing with Wilson when he had made up his mind. The two set out, with their ordinary clothes wrapped in waterproof bundles.

Hope you ain't more of these newspaper reporters, come to scoff. I haven't had any peace since that article and all they do is laugh at me.

We're not reporters, Mister Jay. But we're very interested in the feat performed by Corporal Parr and we'd like to hear your story!

It's the truth, I tell you. I watched Corporal Parr come out of the water. There was a chap made up a poem about it, here's how it goes . . .

35

The bells of Nottsford Church struck three,
As running very fast and free.
The gallant soldier set his pace,
And started on his challenge race.

Then he approached the toll gate door,
The mile he'd run in minutes four.
The toll gate keeper moved the gate,
'Twas here he slowed to walking rate.

The brave soldier strode out in spanking style,
And in minutes less than seven he'd walked a measured mile.
This brought him to the bridge over the river Wyve,
And into the dark waters he took a headlong dive!

Breasting high the whirling foam,
Corporal Parr was now near home.
He finished as the clock struck half past three,
And our hearts o'er-flowed with honest glee.

Now don't you go writing stories making me out to be a daft old stick. Corporal Parr did it—and I saw it!

Don't worry, Mister Jay. I believe you.

The old chap spins a good yarn but surely you don't believe it, Wilson!

Of course I do, Tom. Didn't you notice the constant reference to time throughout the poem. If the times had been inaccurate, people would have been quick to notice.

Vale continued his training and Wilson's unorthodox methods, like running with heavy back-packs, worked wonders. Vale was soon back to his old form, and a few weeks later, he had his first big competitive race since his accident.

That's the fastest time this season. You've really brought Tom back to full fitness, Wilson!

It's Tom's big heart that did it. He had plenty of courage. You'd never, never know he had been injured!

As Wilson congratulated Tom, Frank Ducken, an official of the Amateur Athletics Association arrived.

Run, Tom!

A super mile, Tom! I'd like you to meet Alf Dean. He's got a proposition that might interest you.

Next month, I'm promoting an athletics meeting at Nottsford and I've a notion that should draw a big crowd!

There has been a lot of talk about Corporal Parr's so called athletic feat, so I propose to get a champion miler, a top-rate walker and a record-breaking swimmer and send them over the course. I doubt if their combined times will equal Parr's so-called record, but it will cause a lot of public interest.

I've got Bill Blair, the Midlands walker, and David Malky, our top free-style swimmer, fixed up and I'm hoping Tom here will tackle the mile!

There was only one Corporal Parr! I tell you what. You get three to take part in the contest and I'll try to beat them!

That clinches it! I'll run for you, Mister Dean!

This is terrific— Wilson against Bill Blair and Malky.

And don't forget the clock! He has to do it in half an hour!

37

The concentrated training went on in all sorts of settings. Soon it was time for the challenge . . .

In the square at Nottsford.

I'm glad that's over, but I never felt so fit in my life. You know, Wilson, I almost feel as if I could do this Corporal Parr thing myself!

History is repeating itself. Parr's old Regiment has merged with the Dowcester regiment, and the Colonel has offered to start the race.

History will repeat itself—for Corporal Parr's feat will be repeated also!

At three o' clock exactly . . .

They're off!

We're making good time. We should do the mile in well under four minutes, and get off to a great start!

39

Vale kept going and his fighting heart forced him on, past the point of exhaustion. Tapping hidden reserves of strength, he kept up with the champion swimmer . . .

But I've not come all this way to be beaten!

I've never seen anything like it!

You've done it, Tom! The Nottsford clock is striking half past three right now!

A wonderful feat, Tom! I knew you could do it!

I've never been so exhausted in all my life—and—hey, Wilson, you're walking normally! I thought you'd hurt your leg!

There was never anything wrong with Wilson's leg, Tom. He had to fake that injury. Read this article and you'll understand!

In the opinion of this writer, Wilson will complete the course in half an hour and emulate the feat of the legendary Corporal Parr. But Wilson is a wonder man who can carry off feats outwith the range of ordinary people. No other athlete would stand any chance of performing this feat! This afternoon's event, therefore, will do nothing to confirm the claims of any supporters of the long dead Corporal Parr.

Well done, son. Maybe people will listen to me now. You did it in less than half an hour—and so did Corporal Parr—and I saw you both!

The End 41

GAME FISH AND HOW TO CATCH 'EM

Joe Dodds describes some of Britain's fresh-water fish, and gives a few hints on how to land them.

BROWN TROUT
The brown trout can adapt itself to all sorts of streams and lakes but the biggest fish are to be found in limestone regions. Generally speaking, fly-fishing is accepted as the only sporting way to catch trout but bait fishing with natural nymphs, minnows or redworms is permitted on some waters.

SEA-TROUT
The sea-trout closely resembles the salmon but can be identified by the typical long upper jaw bone of the trout species. It is encountered mainly on the west coast and runs up-river from June onwards through the summer months. The chief methods of fishing for sea-trout are fly-fishing, spinning and worming. A word of warning! Fresh-run sea-trout have very soft mouths and spinning can both damage and lose your fish! Because sea-trout are shy fish the best bags are caught at night when the darkness gives cover for the fisher's movements.

SALMON
Unlike sea-trout, salmon are rarely caught after dark. Salmon do not eat when in the river but live off the fat they have accumulated at sea. This, however, does not prevent them from snapping at the angler's lures. Since mud and sand irritate their gills, salmon are fond of stones and rock bottoms. In addition to fly-fishing and spinning, salmon will take natural baits such as worms, minnows, sand-eels and shrimps.

RAINBOW TROUT
The American rainbow trout was introduced into British waters over seventy years ago. It is a handsome fish with a dark blue-green back and pink markings on its sides. It grows much faster than the native brown trout and feeds more vigorously. Tinsel-dressed flies often attract these fish even when there is little or no natural fly life on the water.

GRAYLING
Although a member of the salmon family, grayling are usually classed as coarse fish. They are at their best in autumn and early winter providing a pleasant extension of the game-fishing season. Grayling usually feed on the bottom but, in certain conditions, will rise for a tempting fly. The wise angler takes both fly and bait tackle when after these fish! Maggots, small redworms and grasshoppers are the best baits.

CAST, HOOK AND STRIKE

S FISHING TACKLE.

BAIT

E. DODDS

Get your gear, Ted. The cod are in! Blokes are catching 'em by the dozen!

That's what I like to hear! Just as well I've got my tackle handy!

JOE DODDS and his grandfather, Ernie, a small-time haulage contractor, were staying over-night at the sea-side town of Radley. As they stopped their truck outside their usual boarding house, Joe heard a welcome cry.

Hey, what do you think you're doing, Joe?

Didn't you hear, Grandad? The cod are in and it's time I was on the beach!

FRESH SEAFOOD. CRABS. EELS. PRAWNS

J LTD.

See you later, Grandad!

Fancy passing up one of Ma Barker's high teas for fishing! Always said there was a worm on one end of the line an' a fool at the other!

43

47

THE END

48

King Cobra

Bill King, world-roving freelance reporter, was visiting a new African republic. Officially he was there to see a bold scheme to turn a vast area of jungle into food-producing land. Unofficially, Bill was acting on a tip-off that a neighbouring country was out to sabotage the land-reclaiming scheme.

If you can clear the land and destroy the weeds in time for the planting season there will be food for everyone next year. But—you have something else to show me?

Yes. You must have friends in high places, Mister King. I have orders to show you something which I thought was top secret.

We've got visitors, and they don't look friendly.

After them. They mustn't get away.

There goes a tyre. We're going into a skid. I can't hold it.

The driver's head was slammed against the windscreen.

It's time for King Cobra to show up!

Bill King's other identity was King Cobra, the world-famous crime-fighter. Now, pulling on cords in his special suit, he inflated his Cobra hood as he swiftly changed into King Cobra.

Got him! We'll float down safely. But we must get out of sight of our pursuers somehow—

The African official recovered quickly.

King Cobra! The crime fighter! How did you get here? What happened to Bill King?

He was thrown clear and he's OK. Listen carefully.

I've set fire to the jeep. You can slip away unseen. Return to your base. Wait until you hear from me by radio.

Using the buoyancy of his helmet, King Cobra set off after his attackers.

They can't have survived that. We can go back to the doctor and report a successful mission.

There's another of the plant monsters. They're springing up all over the place. They must have escaped from somewhere.

I'm not letting those thugs out of my sight. I mean to find out where they came from, and what they're up to.

In a remote jungle valley.

I've a hunch I'm getting near the end of the trail.

Giant greenhouses! What's going on? I must get closer!

The man-killing plants! Breeding by the thousand. The seeds of the ones I've seen must have escaped from here.

Suddenly.

Sound the alarm. Call Doctor Diaz. We've got an intruder.

He can't be human! He's bullet-proof.

King Cobra's fantastic suit could turn aside bullets.

He's gone through the glass wall—

I've got to save him, or that plant will eat him alive.

Hold on! I'll get you free.

King Cobra! You have met your match at last. My creatures will destroy you, just as their seeds will soon destroy this whole country.

You're mad, Diaz. You won't get away with this.

Only you might have stopped me, and you are about to be destroyed. My mission is to wreck this country's plans to turn the jungle into food-producing farmland. When its people are starving they will be invaded and conquered.

King Cobra stepped up the voltage in his power-packed gauntlets.

The plants have become super-charged! They are breaking loose! Run!

The shocked plants released King Cobra.

This is King Cobra! Get your flying weed-killers here— fast. Home in on my radio.

The plants have turned on us. We are doomed.

There's our target. What a hideous sight.

Let's hope our weed-killer is strong enough.

N513E

The terrible plants withered and died immediately.

My job is done. It's time I disappeared.

Come out, Doctor Diaz. You are under arrest.

I was on the verge of success. In a few days I would have loosed milions of my plants and brought the country to ruin. If only King Cobra hadn't interfered—

It was time for Bill King to appear again.

Bill King! You are safe! I haven't seen you since the car crash. King Cobra must have looked after you, too.

Yes, you could say that.

Later.

But King Cobra! What became of him?

You'll never find him. King Cobra never hangs around once his job is done.

The End 55

FANGS TO FIGHT THE MOHAWKS

IN October, 1643, in Canada, the French established Fort Villemarie, about the spot where Ottowa stands today. Captain Henri Maison was in charge of this outpost on the fringe of a dense wilderness, the haunt of the savage Mohawk Indians, who ambushed and slaughtered white settlers every chance they got.

Captain Maison sent back to France for his dogs, and a pack of six came out, with the leader an Alsatian named Pilot. This dog was tireless in its scouting in the woods around the fort, searching out Mohawks. When it tracked down the Redskins it raced back to the fort and gave the alarm. The Mohawks came to hate Pilot.

Then one day Pilot turned renegade—or so the soldiers thought.

The Mohawks attack! Fire the cannon before they reach the fort or they will overwhelm us!

I can't! Pilot has gone mad! He won't let me near the gun!

Earlier that day.

There goes Pilot and his pack on patrol. He can scent a Mohawk a mile away!

IT'S GOALS THAT COUNT

Yours, Don.

NICK SMITH, the world-famous inside-left, played for First Division Stonebury Arsenal early in his career. In the championship, the Arsenal trailed Radford by one point and were due to meet in the season's last game. In the second last game, the Arsenal were playing Oldside. Nick leaped to a high ball—

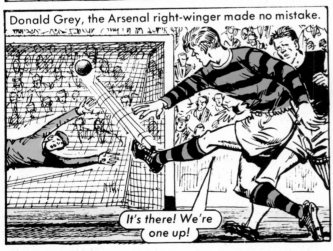

Donald Grey, the Arsenal right-winger made no mistake.

It's there! We're one up!

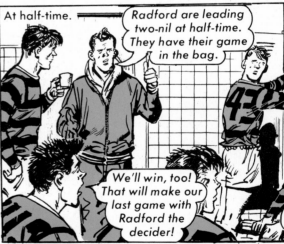

At half-time.

Radford are leading two-nil at half-time. They have their game in the bag.

We'll win, too! That will make our last game with Radford the decider!

Two minutes after the interval, the Arsenal centre-half made a bad mistake.

Yours, Bert—oh, I haven't hit that pass back hard enough.

Its' there! What a gift!

The Arsenal stormed back. Don Grey was prominent in the attack.

Drat! Great save, goalie!

But it was Oldside who went ahead with ten minutes left.

Come on, lads! We've ten minutes left and we've got to get two goals. Let's have an all-out effort!

Eight minutes later, Oldside still led, but Nick found an opening.

Right, Don—it's all yours.

Don hesitated for that vital split second.

What a chance missed. Why didn't Don shoot first-time?

Reg Boulter was Nick's special pal.

What happened back there, Don? That missed chance has cost us the game, and probably the championship. And you were shouting at us to put everything into it—

Sorry, Nick. Sorry, Reg.

But the Arsenal manager had surprising news.

Lads, there's hope for us yet! Radford went down three-two. We can still win the championship by beating them next Saturday. We'll have a week at the seaside preparing for the game. We'll be champs yet.

Am I glad to hear that!

The Arsenal traveled to Brillsea where they played golf to relax.

Gosh, that one's going to finish up pretty near the edge of the cliff, Don.

Mine's out there somewhere, too.

That's mine, nearest. Yours is a bit further on, Don.

Don, what club should—Hey, look out, you'll be over the cliff!

What's wrong with you, Don? You almost walked over the cliff.

Nick, I never saw the edge. Now I'll have to tell you— I'm going blind!

60

So that's why you missed that chance at Oldside!

Yes, Nick, I've been getting spells where everything just becomes a blur. I've been slipping off to Manchester to see a doctor. I'm having treatment but he's not sure what's causing it.

I'll have to tell the boss. I can't play on Saturday and risk missing another vital goal. I'd set my heart on helping the Arsenal to win the Championship, then this had to happen! I'm finished with football, and I'm taking nothing out of it.

Don, say nothing to Mr Wolston. You can play one more game. You say your sight only goes for short spells. Well, Reg and I can train you to cope with that. We'll go to the beach away from the rest of the team. They needn't know.

Later—

Right, Nick. I only hope it works out.

Don, you'll have to wear this blindfold. Reg and I will shoot passes along the ground to you, and clap hands as a signal when the ball's directly in front of you.

There's the signal, Don, the ball's coming up in front of you—now! Tee it up and crack it!

You did it, Don. It can be done. We'll keep practising, in secret, on the beach here, all week! You'll be ready for any blind spell in the match on Saturday.

Saturday afternoon. —

Is your sight right just now, Don?

Yes, Nick, and it could stay that way! I'll let you know if it does go during the match.

Don Grey was in good form.

That's us one up—thanks to Don's great cross. I hope nothing happens to him today. It means so much to him.

But Radford were soon on level terms.

Then the Arsenal centre-forward took a bad knock.

Don, you move into the centre and the substitute can take your place on the wing.

It's happened, Nick! Everything's gone blurred.

Right, Don, I'll signal Reg and let him know.

Then, near full time, with the score still a draw—

Don, stop now! The goal's straight ahead. I've got to go and help Reg.

They've got Don covered. I'll hold on to the ball a bit longer.

Good, I've drawn the centre-half from Don.

Nick whipped the ball back to Reg.

Keep running forward, Don.

I've got the inside pass. Now we'll know if all our special training has paid off . . .

Now then, Don!

Don has heard the signal! He's teeing-up the ball!

What a goal—and the crowd don't realise just how good—for it was scored by a blind man.

That was the winning goal.

UP THE ARSENAL

ARSEN FOR TH

Don, you're the hero of the team. Our plan paid off. You won the Championship for us!

Yes, Nick, thanks to you and Reg. My sight won't let me play football again, but I can go out of the game happy. I helped the Arsenal to win the Championship!

The End

Later...

GRAND ANTIQUE SALE

COME ALONG AFTER BASE

JAKE'S BARN

I hereby declare this great antique sale open—and you good people are in for a treat!

Gee, will you get a load of that—all this great stuff—and get a load of the faces of Gold Brick Brogan and Smooth Talkin' Carter!

How come, Bernard? I thought everything worth a cent had been taken out and sold long ago.

Maybe so, mate. But this used to be a livery stable and the harness room had been blocked with rubbish for years. I just unblocked it, and found the treasure trove.

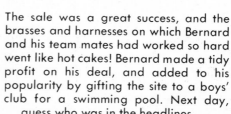

The sale was a great success, and the brasses and harnesses on which Bernard and his team mates had worked so hard went like hot cakes! Bernard made a tidy profit on his deal, and added to his popularity by gifting the site to a boys' club for a swimming pool. Next day, guess who was in the headlines . . .

65

wide open!

67

TONTARA TRIBUNE

GUESS WHO CONNED THE CON MEN?

YES, ITS BRIGGS THE LIMEY GOALIE

AND GUESS WHO PUT THE...

Next night.

It was never like this at the old City ground. Come on, lads, we'll take these Idaho All-Stars apart!

It's there! I caught them on the hop!

GOAL! BRIGGS SCORES

A few minutes later.

Watch him! Get ready to tackle as he dribbles away!

Not this time, mate! There are other ways—

Now—a long throw up field and a chase!

He's fast—but he didn't expect this move—and I did!

Got it! Now to teach that goalie it's naughty to get too far out of his goal!

But don't go away, good folks. The show ain't over yet. Now we have a special presentation by our own Tontara Tigers!

Please accept our Rookie of the Year award, Bernard. You sure earned it the way you put it over Blue Lightning and the Cowboys!

Thanks, Joe. It was a most enjoyable game of rounders!

Next day.

Sorry to see you go, Bernard. But thanks for helping me out!

Hey, look, what's this? Don't tell me Blue Lightning's in town again!

This time, it's for you, Bernard! You've put soccer on the map in this town in a big way!

BRIGGS the GREATEST

The End

BERNARD'S BALL GAME

Be like Bernard Briggs—play baseball! The rules have been simplified for this table-top game, but it should give you a bit of fun.

The game is played between two teams, each of 9 men. The object is to score more runs than the opposing team. A run is scored when the batter reaches home base, or plate, having gone round the other 3 bases.

The game consists of 9 innings. An innings is completed when three men are out from each team.

The batting team has the counters, nine of them (shirt buttons are ideal). The pitching team has the dice.

When the pitcher throws the dice, the batters each move according to the number thrown.

The batters have the option of stopping at or going past a base if the pitcher throws a high enough number.

As many batters as desired can be on the pitch at one time. All must start from the "batter's box" which is immediately before the home base. All must move when the pitcher throws the dice—and follow the instructions on the box where they land. Now go and have fun.

71

TOM BASS

BUSH PILOT

IN the early days of aviation, young Tom Bass, an American, made his living by flying his aeroplane. With his pet raccoon, Rocky, Tom was prepared to fly anywhere to earn a few dollars. His staple business was giving joy rides but, as planes became more commonplace in America, business fell off.

We haven't even done enough business in this town to pay the petrol, Rocky. It's time we took the plane somewhere else.

JOY RIDE
$10 $5
$2.50.

In New York.

It's Brazil for us, Rocky. One day, people will fly to Brazil and it will be ships that take second place . . .

Eventually, hundreds of miles up the Amazon.

This is Manaus, Rocky. A busy trading city—in the middle of the jungle!

A racetrack served as an airfield.

Take me first!

I'll pay fifty dollars!

H...h...hey! One at a time! Gosh, the people of Manaus are crazy about aeroplanes!

It was a good idea to come here. This is good business!

By nightfall. Another few days like today and we'll be rich, Rocky. You sleep here and look after the plane . . .

Rocky was a good guard, but there were some things even the best guards missed.

In the morning. My plane! Termites have eaten all the fabric!

The plane was still sound in its structure.

It'll be a fortnight before new supplies of dope and fabric can be shipped here. What will I do in the meantime?

Look out! That plank—

Sorry about that, senor.

What happened? A wooden beam that big should have flattened me—

Not this wood, senor. It is the lightest wood in the world—balsa!

The lightest wood in the world, eh? That gives me an idea . . .

Tom bought some balsa wood.

H'mmm . . . this wood works easily, too, Rocky!

Just as I thought— one can make toys that actually fly . . .

I want one! I want one!

In the fortnight he had to wait, Tom did a roaring trade.

Some of these kids may grow up to be the aviators of the future—thanks to a cheap toy getting them interested.

Finally the supplies arrived.

Do I have the honour of encountering the intrepid aviator Thomas Bass?

I'm Tom Bass, yes. What can I do for you?

I am Baron d'Ombey, the map-maker. I want to map the course of the Amazon—and your plane is the ideal vehicle!

Sounds more interesting than giving joy rides. Make it worth my while, Baron, and I'm with you!

Phew, we were lucky to find this clear strip, in a tropical rain forest!

Uh-huh—it managed to damage a wing. We'll have to land and repair the rip or the whole wing could go!

The landing did not pass unnoticed.

The wing was soon repaired, but . . .

I took no chances—I brought enough fabric to cover both these wings. We'll soon be airborne again.

Er . . . Tom. We've got company!

I gather the chief wants to fly in the "big bird" . . . or else!

Well, I've given joy rides before—and he's got a powerful argument!

Another satisfied customer—

Get aboard, Baron and let's get out of here!

They . . . er . . . seem to prefer that we should stay, for a while!

Gold! Must be ancient stuff! They want to buy the plane, Tom!

Nothing doing. The gold is worth far more than my plane—but we couldn't get it back to Manaus!

You are so right, Tom. But the chief seems very keen to acquire an aeroplane.

Mmm, well—I know, tell him we'll make him a plane of his own!

This is madness, Tom. Even if we succeed in making a plane, how can we find an engine for it in the jungle?

Who said anything about an engine? We'll make him a glider! This balsa wood is easy to work.

Nearly done. We won't need anything fancy like ailerons . . .

Now he wants to see that it flies, like the other bird.

I was wondering about that. I suppose it'll have to be done . . .

They'll keep you here as hostage, Baron—so we've both got to hope I can get this thing up in the air!

Made it—by inches!

See, chief! Both birds fly!

Tom landed safely.

Let's get out of here, quick, Baron. The chief is likely to get mad when he finds his bird is earthbound without this one!

I've got the gold! We worked for it!

Sorry, fellas! Time to go home!

Some of those arrows came close!

Too close! One of them's holed the petrol tank!

Later, on a mud-flat.

That's the hole patched up—but we don't have enough petrol to get us back to Manaus!

Then we're done for! If the jaguars don't get us, the Indians will!

There is one chance . . . the river got us out here—perhaps it can get us back! D'you see those logs?

Balsa wood. It isn't only light—it floats well.

It's a chance in a hundred—but they're better odds than we'd have on foot . . .

Some days later . . .

The End 79

OLD-TIMERS OF THE SEVEN SEAS

In the 1880's, vast, iron-hulled square-riggers plied the hazardous Cape Horn routes to Australia and Western America. The outward-bound cargoes were generally coal and railway iron, and they came back laden with grain, timber and nitrates. The crews were often away for years.

Small, single-hatch coasters, with coal-fired boilers and open bridges, were in operation for almost 80 years until motor ships took over just before World War II. Having shallow draughts, they were able to use almost any harbour and they had stout rubbing strakes around the hulls.

Water-tube, coal-fired boilers, 3,700 horse power reciprocating engines and vast coal bunkers left only very cramped quarters for the crew of this 27-knot torpedo boat destroyer of the 1890's. It had two turn-table-mounted torpedo tubes and one fixed in the bows, a 12-pounder gun and several smaller quick-firers.

British-built in 1900, this coal-fired ice-breaker was used by the Russians in the Arctic Ocean and the Baltic. Reinforced hull plating combined with three propellers aft and one forward enabled it to force a passage through very heavy ice.

PARKER'S BARKERS

Pete Parker ran a dogs' home. One day—

Yes, lads, you need new kennels but we're short of cash, so—

I can't even hammer a nail in straight. There must be some other way—

Are you Parker? Special delivery, mate.

Plastic glue—the very thing. I wonder who sent it?

There now, the last kennel done. Oh, oh, here comes the rain!

Later

Wow! That glue is rising like dough! It's taking the roofs off the kennels!

Where are you off to? Steady on, lads.

Huh! Might have known they wouldn't sleep out in the wet. What a hard floor!

Next day

Ah! Here's the Parker my special plastic glue was delivered to. Say, what a super shape. Just what I need for my new studio!

What do I do with this stuff now?

That was Pinto Parker, the famous modeller. He was so glad to get his plastic glue back he gave me all this money.

And I know just what to do with it.

I'll have that!

Hey, Bloodhound Bill, what are you up to?

You're a police dog, you're not supposed to pinch things.

Follow Bill, lads. He's on to something good.

Like a boneyard, maybe?

Puff! Pant! A builder's yard! What are my dogs doing in here?

Later.

How about that! They've bought made-to-measure kennels. Everyone's happy!

82

The End

And it tastes good and cool. But to carry umbrellas for that! You are poor, simple fools!

Help yourselves! Two each! These Burmese peasants should pay a toll!

Umbrellas indeed! And when our guards on the other side take some, there won't be many melons left to keep cool!

Your men must pay, Tuan! Me poor man. Need money for melons!

Conquerors don't pay! On your way and be thankful we didn't take them all!

But, halfway across the bridge . . .

Hold it! Come, Chung! Time for work!

Only seconds to go! Come on, Chung!

Hey-ho! Run, you foolish beasts! Run for your lives!

TALK ABOUT LUCK

The Danny Boyd story starting opposite is all about the luckiest golfer Danny ever met. Here's our artist's impression of some other lucky, and not so lucky, golf course incidents.

BOBBY'S LUCKY BOUNCE. American golfer, Bobby, Cruickshank, delighted when his ball bounced off a rock and away from a waiting pond, threw his club into the air.

BOBBY'S BAD BREAK. But that was where Bobby's luck changed. The club came down again—right on top of his head.

"YACHT" TO SEE IT. An Army and Navy team, playing the Royal Thames Yacht Club at Sunningdale in May 1930, drove their ball into a bunker. The yachtsmen's ball followed—and bounced right out again! It had struck the Army and Navy ball.

KICK BACK. An English golfer holed his approach shot. His delight was short-lived. The ball suddenly reappeared, kicked by a surprised frog.

MID-SURREY MADNESS. In 1945, at Royal Mid-Surrey, a golfer's ball was fanned into the hole by the flapping wings of a terrified grouse.

TROUT CLOUT. A golfer on Kilarney course in Ireland wasn't having any "birdies" on a day in June 1957. But he got a fish when his sliced ball knocked out a trout rising from one of the lakes to take a fly.

TEE-RIFFIC SHOT!

DANNY BOYD

GOLF STAR IN THE MAKING

YOUNG Danny Boyd was hard up—as usual. He was a professional golfer and he had used his last five pounds to enter a pro-am competition.

Hey, son, want a lift? Are you going to the pro-am?

Thanks. Seems to be a long road to that Golden Gate!

Don't stamp on the floor, son. You'll go right through. Old Bessie here will just about get us to the Golden Gate before she packs in for good!

She's certainly seen better days.

The driver, Arthur Perkins, was a twenty-four handicap player.

That's the place! Let's have a look!

What at?

You can't practise on the course during the competition, Arthur. You'll disqualify yourself.

Here we are, lad! The seventeenth hole of Golden Gate. Get a hole in one here, and you win a car! If no one gets a hole in one, the bloke nearest the hole gets a hundred quid. Let's 'ave a trial run.

Well, I wouldn't want that, Danny. I need that car.

Later, at the Golden Gate clubhouse.

See you, Arthur—and thanks for the lift.

No sweat, son. We'll ride in style, going away!

Inside the clubhouse the officials were making the draw.

The worst thing about this competition is that anyone with a fiver can enter.

Pair that Yorkshire character, Perkins, with the boy, Boyd. We can't inflict them on anyone else.

90

The 17th hole.

Here we are then, Danny! One car coming up—and there's another one to win tomorrow!

I'll see what I can do.

WIN A CAR!

Danny's shot was very close.

Six inches! That's the nearest yet, and this is the last couple. That lad could win a hundred pounds.

Then it was Arthur's turn.

I-it's bounced off the prize car . . .

PRIZE

Eee, lad, I've done it! I won a car.

Well done, Arthur. That must be the strangest hole in one ever.

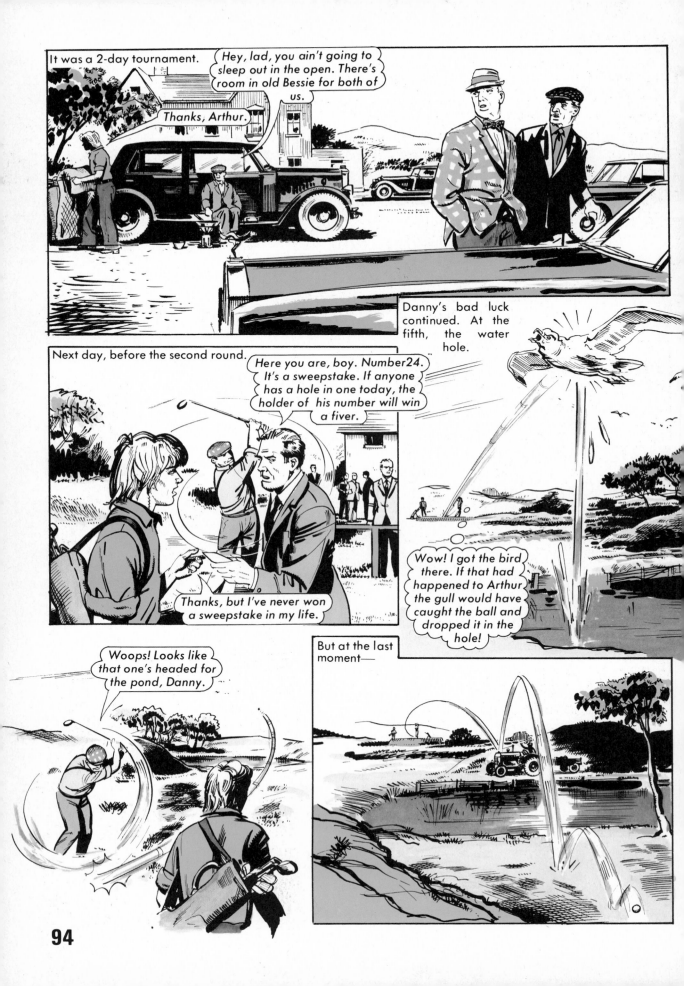

Danny's score was nowhere near the prize list, but—

THE END

The COONSKIN GRENADIER

ZEBADIAH FLOOD, from the Great Smoky Mountains of Carolina had found an ancient Royal Warrant which gave him the rank of Honorary Colonel in the Royal Grenadiers (King George's Own). It was World War II, and Colonel Sir John Grogham, commander of Potomac Depot, kept trying to " lose " Zeb on overseas postings. Now, returned from the East Indies, Zebadiah had with him Alexander, a friendly baboon.

Dear son—I takes pen in hand to say as we all and the hogs is fine and miss you. Some Yankees come calling and said you was drafted, but I said they was not to call you names and chased them off with my old scattergun . . .

'E's been drafted, called up, Sir John, by the Americans. The answer to our problem. And there is a sergeant what I know in the Hamerican forces—

Egad, Sarn't-Major. This is great. Help yourself to a cigar.

Zeb was given a mission.

Sir John, sure is obliging of you to loan Alexander and me your own automobile, and the sergeant-major to drive it.

Not at all, me boy. Just want to make sure you get where you are going.

Sarn't-Major, I sure hope Sir John don't worry about us getting back in time for that guard on Buckingham Palace.

No, Honorary Colonel, I don't think as 'e is at all worried about that.

Later . . . Norfolk way.

101 TRANSPORT GROUP U.S. 8th AIR FORCE

Royal Grenadiers, on a courtesy visit.

Yeah. Staff Runkel's expecting you.

HALT

98

Need any help, Staff Runkel?

To handle one draft-dodger? You must be joking, boy.

GUARD ROOM

It's crashing. Hey, that kite's a German one!

Zeb was first to the downed aircraft.

Cousin, you better get out before this heap takes fire.

Thank you. I am thinking the same.

You must use up a lot of aireyplanes if you always land 'em like that.

I was hit by flak. The Luftwaffe pursue me. Sir, I have information of much importance for your military command.

I am not German. My name is Teodor Pilsudski—once major of Polish Air Force, now agent of the Warsaw Underground.

OK, buster, you'll get a chance to prove your story. Lock him up, boys.

Now to get back to you—er, Honorary Colonel. How'd you like to inspect the guard?

A tolerable turn-out, cousin.

Now maybe you'd care to look over the guardroom, Honorary Colonel.

ARDROOM

101

Yonder is the airfield where the stolen plane was observed to land. You have all studied your pictures of the fugitive who must be liquidated?

Ja, Herr Oberleutnant.

Meanwhile, in 101 Transport guardroom—

Cut that racket.

But, cousin, this child is hungry.

This here jail is pure comfort, but right now I'd admire to have some vittles.

Buster, you eat when we decide. Now shaddup—

Pardon, sir. Your monkey stole the keys of the guard.

Not stole—borrowed. Alexander is honest, except with bananas.

Two M.P's had a shock—

Your keys, cousin. Me an' Alexander and the Polish gent is going out to eat.

What! Get 'em . . .

I needs my vittles!

102

Near the field perimeter.

Looks like that guy wants for us to stop.

Blooming Yanks! Can't he see we're in an 'urry?

HALT

Hus Royal Grenadiers don't stop for no Colonials . . .

Looks like my iron nerve and quick thinking got you out of that 'ot spot, Honorary Colonel.

Sure did, Sergeant-Major—but it seems like we are being followed.

Shoot!

Omigosh—bullets! Them 'orrible 'uns is firing at us.

Doggone them square-heads! They've sure mussed up Colonel Sir John's fine automobile. So—

My information is safe. Now I must tell it to one of high rank.

Maybe you should see my friend, General Lord Golightly. He's the big chief of us Royal Grenadiers.

Next day, at Potomac Barracks.

Now we'll never get rid of that backwoods oaf, Sarn't-Major. He's become a confounded hero. And also, how did my car get in such a state!

Sorry, sir. It just sort of 'appened.

Zeb met a " Very Important Person ".

Suh, it's right kindly of you to offer me a medal, but I'll settle for some of them cigars to send back to my maw.

Sensible choice, m'boy. I'll have a box of 'em posted to the dear lady.

The End

JUNKERS " JU 88." The " backbone " of the Luftwaffe, 15,000 of these planes were built between 1939 and 1945. The JU 88 owed much of its success to American design and construction techniques, and appeared in many different variations.

GERMAN WARPLANES ✠

JUNKERS " JU 87." A two-seater dive-bomber, the well-armed but comparatively slow " Stuka " carried a 2200 lb. bomb load. 255 m.p.h. was its maximum speed.

FIESLER " FI 156 " STORCH (STORK). Designed as a general communications and reconnaissance aircraft, the " Storch " was also employed in staff transport and ambulance duties. During the war, it was manufactured in German-controlled factories in Occupied France and Czechoslovakia. Its top speed was only 109 m.p.h.

MESSERSCHMITT " BF 109." This well-known fighter packed a " punch " of two machine-guns in the engine cowling, one in each wing and a 20 mm. cannon firing through the propeller boss. Top speed was 354 m.p.h.

MESSERSCHMITT " BF 110." This twin-engined fighter-bomber could carry a bomb load of 3920 lb. at almost 360 m.p.h. A pilot, navigator and rear-gunner made up its crew.

HEINKEL " HE 111." The Luftwaffe's first modern medium bomber, the " HE 111 " was the mainstay of the German bombing offensive during the Battle of Britain. Bomb load, 5510 lb. Maximum speed, 258 m.p.h.

The RIDDLE OF RATSPEL PASS

IN 1944, R.A.F. aircrews trying to knock out the ball-bearing factory at Felsbach, at the end of Ratspel Pass, in Southern Germany, brought back strange tales, saying they could not get through. Three Mosquitos were making the latest attempt!

Look, skipper, the sky's suddenly full of little balloons—and we're being attacked by an old triplane.

It's a Fokker triplane—a World War I fighter. We'd better climb to get away from, these balloons!

Where did this cloud come from all of a sudden?

But as the Mosquitos climbed—

Skipper, the cloud—it's covering all our windows, like sticky cotton-wool!

It's affecting the controls too! Everything has gone sluggish! We must climb out of this!

Phew! We made it into clear air! We can see again and the plane's OK again.

We're going home. The riddle of Ratspell Pass will have to be solved before Felsbach can be attacked.

The R.A.F. called in Sergeant Tim Morgan of the Military Police who specialised in solving battlefield mysteries.

Sergeant Morgan, the sooner you solve the riddle of the Ratspel Pass, the better.

Right, sir, I'm on my way.

The next day, Sergeant Morgan flew towards Felsbach in a captured German spotter plane, and in the uniform of a German artillery officer.

There's Felsbach ahead. I'll make an apparent crash landing near the factory, then use a bit bluff to do some investigating.

Morgan noticed the balloons too late.

The balloons! I should have been paying more attention.

There goes my prop. I'll have to make my forced landing sooner than I thought.

The ground's really bumpy here, but it's the only clear space—

Later—

I am Leutnant Mauer, Field Artillery. Where am I? I crashed in my Storch and—

Do not waste your time, and ours. You are a British spy. You're in the guardroom at the Felsbach ball-bearing factory. Your papers are excellent forgeries but while being brought here after the crash you spoke in English.

109

You were muttering something about an old aeroplane. Now, why did you come here?

You tell me, what are the small balloons? Who flies the old Fokker triplane? What goes on in the Ratspel Pass?

Ach, the balloons! The Fokker! It's old Count Von Rothberg! The old crackpot must have put the wind up the Allied intelligence with his games.

He's an old crank who lives on what's left of his family estate. Used to own all the Ratspel Pass. Flies around in his last war Fokker and plays with weather balloons.

It takes more than that to stop British bombers.

British bombers? Yes, they have come up the pass, but they always seem to turn away. Are you saying they were stopped by something? Is that why you came here?

The riddle of the pass is as much a mystery to you as to me. I can't let you find the answer first!

It must have been Fritz. Something in the Ratspel Pass, to do with Von Rothberg. The old man is a bit of a scientist. He may have come up with something. Thank you, Britisher.

Aargh!

Got them! Now to get out of here!

Other SS men will have been alerted by the shots. I'll head for the woods.

Once in the woods, I must make for Castle Rothberg, back in the Ratspel pass.

I've come to the right place! It's all here at Castle Rothberg.

Count Von Rothberg, I am a British agent. The SS are coming after me. You have a secret they want—and must not get!

What secret?

My Nazi pals! How dare you class me with those scoundrels!

How you stopped the British bombers with that stuff in the clouds. You send it up in those balloons, don't you? If your Nazi pals get hold of that—

As for shooting at the British bombers, I am a German airman and it is my duty to fight them if I can. In the last war I accounted for 27 of your fighters. But I am also opposed to these present-day SS thugs.

I believe you, sir.

I send up my balloons with chemicals designed to prevent rain-fall—not bombers.

You don't know, then, that your chemicals cause a frothy substance that ices up an aircraft's vision and controls? The SS will use your experiments to prolong this war. Look, they're coming now.

Could you fly my Fokker to escape? I have an old Albatros plane I could use for further experiments.

I could fly the Fokker—I must!

In those balloons are all my stock of chemicals. You have my word I will make no more until this war is over.

I understand, sir. I'll try to take care of your Fokker, and return it one day.

It is the British spy! He is after the balloons! Stop him!

The Count will be able to claim he was unable to stop me stealing his plane and destroying all his work. And as for you SS swine—

It's all over. I'll head down the Pass for the nearest allied base.

Presently—

It's the Count in his Albatros fighter. He's come to wave me goodbye. He's quite a man!

The next day Mosquitos came in and flattened the Felsbach ball-bearing factory. The riddle of Ratspel pass was solved.

The End

One hot summer's day in 1851, a strange trio was crossing the dusty Nevada plains.

That ranch is on the main road to town, Ben. We'll see if the owner will let us put up our tent and give a show.

THE MAN'S A MARVEL

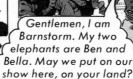

Gentlemen, I am Barnstorm. My two elephants are Ben and Bella. May we put on our show here, on your land?

Give your show and welcome. The land won't be mine for much longer anyway. Give him a hand, Buck.

Who is that young feller and what did he mean?

He's Tom Mason. He's been badly hit by cattle rustling and he'll have to sell his ranch to a bloke called ned Carley, who holds a mortgage on it.

It's a pity his father, Jim, was killed before Tom arrived here. Jim and old Butch Blake were supposed to have discoverd a gold mine. But Jim was shot before he could tell anyone where the mine was. Old Butch hasn't been seen since.

The big tent had been seen by passing cowboys and the next afternoon—

Roll up! Roll up! Be killed by Deadshot Dugan, serenaded by Signor Howli, mesmerised by Monsieur Miraldo and entertained by many wonderful artists.

What's he talking about? He doesn't have anyone else with him!

If he says they're there, then I guess they are!

The show started . . .

First, ladies and gentlemen, I will demonstrate my power over my two friends, Ben and Bella. They will obey my every command. Come, Ben. Bow to the audience.

I said . . . ow!

Why you . . . aagh!

Ah, well, music is supposed to soothe the savage beast so I now call upon Signor Howli to sing for you.

Now for a quick change.

O sole mio.

Ooh! He's miles off key!

Ho-ho! The elephants don't like his singing either.

114

Another quick change later . . .

I guess the Signor has skedaddled. I'm Deadshot Dugan so I'll show you a few gun tricks.

You couldn't even hit the side of one of these elephants!

Carley's the name and I bet you can't hit this dime when I throw it up.

Ned Carley was wrong!

He's done it!

Now perhaps you'll sit down and shut up, Mr. Carley!

There followed an amazing display of gunmanship.

Then it was Monsieur Miraldo's turn.

Yah! Anyone could do that.

Now I would like to borrow your watch and shoot it to pieces.

Fire away! I know it's all a trick anyway!

I hope you didn't want it back!

What the—?

Early next morning . . .

Never mind, Jim. Old Butch Blake will look after the mine.

Butch Blake! That was the partner of Tom Mason's father!

Hey, old-timer.

What . . . ? Who . . . ?

You're just after our mine. Take that!

I can't take any chances with him! Ben! Bella!

Oof!

Well done, Bella!

I'm a friend of Tom Mason. Are you all right?

I am now! Sorry I fired at you but I reckon I must have gone a bit crazy after seeing Jim killed. It's all come back now!

You saw the killer?

I'd recognise him again. We were on our way to get help, the mine entrance had caved in, and we ran into a bunch of rustlers. The leader killed Jim and I had my skull creased.

The End

THE UMBRELLA MEN

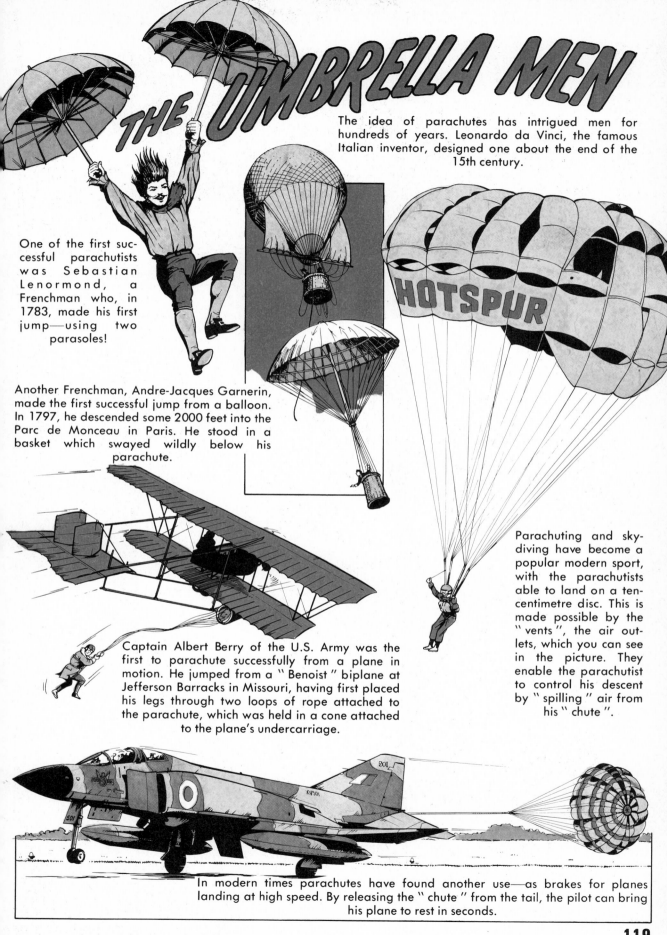

The idea of parachutes has intrigued men for hundreds of years. Leonardo da Vinci, the famous Italian inventor, designed one about the end of the 15th century.

One of the first successful parachutists was Sebastian Lenormond, a Frenchman who, in 1783, made his first jump—using two parasoles!

Another Frenchman, Andre-Jacques Garnerin, made the first successful jump from a balloon. In 1797, he descended some 2000 feet into the Parc de Monceau in Paris. He stood in a basket which swayed wildly below his parachute.

HOTSPUR

Parachuting and sky-diving have become a popular modern sport, with the parachutists able to land on a ten-centimetre disc. This is made possible by the " vents ", the air outlets, which you can see in the picture. They enable the parachutist to control his descent by " spilling " air from his " chute ".

Captain Albert Berry of the U.S. Army was the first to parachute successfully from a plane in motion. He jumped from a " Benoist " biplane at Jefferson Barracks in Missouri, having first placed his legs through two loops of rope attached to the parachute, which was held in a cone attached to the plane's undercarriage.

In modern times parachutes have found another use—as brakes for planes landing at high speed. By releasing the " chute " from the tail, the pilot can bring his plane to rest in seconds.

Dive for it, Chung! Here comes the bridge!

The WOLF of KABUL

CONTINUED FROM PAGE 87.

USING the out-size umbrellas as parachutes, the Wolf and Chung floated down towards the river as the bridge disintegrated.

Should be safe enough to come up for air now!

Good, the bridge has gone! The Japs are shooting but we'll soon be round the bend of the river!

They swam strongly and soon reached the prearranged landing place . . .

And they were right . . .

We shall burn those two dogs out!

Bombs, Chung! But no explosions?

Incendiaries! Run, Chung! Run for your life!

The fire's catching up! We're doomed unless—Wait, those elephants! Come, Chung!

122

That's it, Chung! Another Jap down to Clicky-ba!

The Wolf and Chung weaved through the traffic jam of Japs and, with the cloud of dust they threw up few saw them until it was too late. They soon reached the open road.

Half an hour later . . .

One more river to cross— and there's the bridge!

Halt! Show your papers . . . Aargh!

Get ready, Chung! Japs ahead!